# R-LORD

Along with allowing him to breathe in space, Star-Lord's mask has a load of different vision modes, including thermal and ultraviolet.

Star-Lord's blasters are keyed to his DNA and only work in his hands. He can also use them as makeshift jet thrusters to move around in space.

**REAL NAME:** PETER QUILL
**SPECIES:** HUMAN
**OCCUPATION:** INTERGALACTIC ADVENTURER
**SKILLS:** HAND-TO-HAND COMBAT, EXPERT MARKSMAN AND A KEEN STRATEGIST
**LIKES:** AWESOME MUSIC
**DISLIKES:** BEING TOLD WHAT TO DO!

## MUSIC MIX!

His personal stereo and Awesome Mixtape Vol 1 are Star-Lord's only reminders of his time on Earth. They are his most prized possessions and he'll do anything to keep them safe!

THE MILANO.
DEEP SPACE.

MORNIN' GAMMIE. HOW'S SPACE?

## "SO VERY YOUNG"

**MAIRGHREAD SCOTT**
WRITER

**ADAM ARCHER**
ARTIST

**ANDY ELDER**
COLORIST

**VC's JC**
LETTERING

**"STAR-LORD"** BASED ON THE ANIMATED SHORT

ADAPTED BY **JOE CARAMAGNA**

**SEBASTIAN GIRNER & JON MOISAN**
EDITORS **MARK PANICCIA** SENIOR EDITOR
**AXEL ALONSO** EDITOR IN CHIEF **JOE QUESADA**
CHIEF CREATIVE OFFICER **DAN BUCKLEY** PUBLISHER
**ALAN FINE** EXECUTIVE PRODUCER

SPACE CONTINUES TO BE AN INFINITE VOID OF SILENCE AND DESTRUCTION. AND DON'T *EVER* CALL ME THAT AGAIN, PETER QUILL.

FAIR ENOUGH. HOW'S EVERYTHING ELSE?

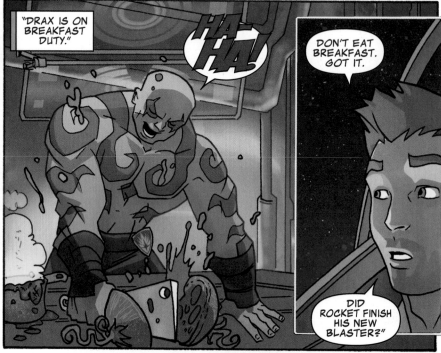

"DRAX IS ON BREAKFAST DUTY."

HA HA!

DON'T EAT BREAKFAST. GOT IT.

DID ROCKET FINISH HIS NEW BLASTER?

"YES. HE'S NOW OBSESSING OVER COLOR CHOICES."

I AM GROOT.

I KNOW, BUT I'M GOING FOR MORE OF A "PURE AGONY" KINDA VIBE.

TCK Zz

THAT ALMOST SOUNDS LIKE ONE OF THE ENGINES GOING OUT...

# CONTENTS

Guardians of the Galaxy Annual 2018 is published by Panini Publishing, a division of Panini UK Limited. Office of publication: Panini UK Ltd. Brockbourne House, 77 Mount Ephraim, Tunbridge Wells, Kent, TN4 8BS. MARVEL, GUARDIANS OF THE GALAXY and all related characters: TM & © 2017 Marvel Entertainment, LLC and its subsidiaries. Licensed by Marvel Characters B.V. www.marvel.com. All rights reserved. No similarity between any of the names, characters, persons and/or institutions in this edition with those of any living or dead person or institution is intended, and any such similarity which may exist is purely coincidental. This publication may not be sold, except by authorised dealers, and is sold subject to the condition that it shall not be sold or distributed with any part of its cover or markings removed, nor in a mutilated condition. This publication is produced under licence from Marvel Characters, Inc. through Panini S.p.A. Printed in Italy. ISBN: 978-1-84653-232-0

© 2017 MARVEL

FSC

www.fsc.org

MIX

Paper from responsible sources

FSC® C005461

STA

The legendary Star-Lord might possibly be the greatest intergalactic hero you've (probably) never heard of. Don't believe us?

**Just read on...**

# PIRATE IN TRAINING!

Kidnapped from Earth when he was just a boy, Peter Quill was raised in space by the pirate-like Ravagers. Taken under the wing of the gang's leader Yondu, he soon learned all the tricks he'd ever need to hustle his way from one side of the galaxy to the other!

# A LITTLE GOOD A LITTLE BAD!

But now he's the leader of the Guardians, Peter Quill has put his days as a scoundrel behind him... kind of. Let's just say that sometimes saving the galaxy means having to break the rules – and that's one thing this intrepid adventurer knows all about!

GUARDIANS

# MILANO

Star-Lord's ship, the Milano, is now the Guardians' mobile headquarters. It's one of the fastest ships in the galaxy, able to outmanoeuvre and outgun everything from Nova Corps Starblasters to Kree Dreadnoughts.

GAMORA! WAIT!

HOLD UP, QUILL! THIS IS MORE IMPORTANT!

I FOUND THIS WHILE I WAS REPAIRING THE SHIP. IT'S A THIEVES' TOOL, CALLED A *SHORT-OUT TICK*. IT GETS INTO A SHIP'S ENGINE AND FRIES IT FROM INSIDE!

WE DIDN'T CRASH, QUILL. SOMEBODY KNOCKED US OUTTA THE SKY!

WE'VE GOTTA GET--

I DON'T THINK YOU'RE GOIN' ANYWHERE, MR. STAR-LORD, SIR.

NOT UNLESS YOUR FRIEND DON'T LIKE HIS FUR NO MORE.

WHAT DO YOU WANT FROM US?

NOTHIN'.

"WE'VE ALREADY GOT YOUR SHIP. AND YOUR CREW."

THIS "TIE UP GAME" IS NO LONGER AMUSING. RELEASE ME!

"THAT'S HOW WE STAY IN BUSINESS. TAKING SHIPS, SELLING PARTS. BUT DORN AND HIS BIKERS TOOK HALF OUR UNITS EVEN THOUGH WE DID ALL THE WORK."

"YOU TALL FOLK ALWAYS THINK WE'RE KIDS AND YOU STILL TAKE WHAT'S OURS."

ONCE GAMORA GETS RID'A THEM, WE DON'T GOTTA SHARE OUR UNITS WITH NO ONE.

OH, NO!

THE END

# TRACER

SKRULL

YOTAT

THANOS

THE SIGNAL HAS BEEN TRACED AS COMING FROM THIS SHIP AND IT'S ESCAPING!

THANE

TERRAX

BLASTAAR

GARA

Who's on board?
Answer here:

Answers on page 61

# ASK DRAX

He's an intergalactic warrior with the muscles to match, and he's here to answer **YOUR** questions! (assuming you're calling from outside Earth)

**Hey Drax,**

**I think you're really cool! I wanted to ask... who'd you choose to cover your back in a fight?**

**Boogal Phanch**
*from the Gamma Quadrant*

*Greeting Boogal. Cool? Why did you assume my body temperature had been lowered? I prefer to fight barechested to show off my tattoos. No covering of the back is needed.*

*Thanks*
**DRAX**

**Yo Drax!**
**Did you ever have hair? I'm totally down with your style!**

**P-GEEX**
*Alpha Centauri System*

*P-GEEX,*
*Yes but I move faster in combat without hair, and more courageously so I am, how do you say, more... bold. I am sorry my style has brought you down.*
**DRAX**

**DRAX! I am hiding in the shadows, waiting upon your move. I am the wind, the rain, the sun. My computer system sees you. My Bio-Mother sees you. I AM EVERYONE.**

**Nang Chankethetteteth** (*with a silent B*)

*Nang,*
*I literally have no idea what you're talking about*
**DRAX**

**Drax,**
**I'm sending you five centroids of copper cable, twenty metroids of titanium line and four of steel.**

**Please confirm**

**Jeleb 10-Feezer**

*Jeleb,*
*I think you've got your wires crossed.*
**DRAX**

**Drax,**
⟡⟐⟡⟊⟒⟒⟟ ⟐⟒ ⟟⟊⟟⟐⟒⟒⟊ **TERRAFORM THE DEMI-GOD** ⟒⟐⟊⟒⟟⟊ ⟊ ⟊⟐⟊⟐⟒ ⟒ **MAXIMUM VOLUME** ⟒⟟⟊ ⟒⟊⟟ ⟊⟊⟒⟊⟊ ⟊ ⟊ ⟊ ⟒⟊ **TIN DEPOSITS OF THE KNEE.**

**Zeb K MolderMeen**
*Nexus*

*Zeb,*
*Your translator isn't working and you're weird anyway.*
**DRAX**

# SEARCH THE STARS!

Star-Lord's ship needs its data bank files to be up to speed. Find all of the names in the grid and circle them....

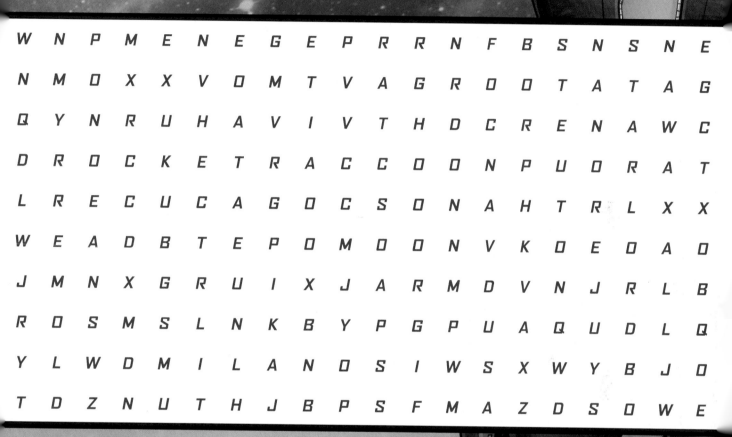

```
W N P M E N E G E P R R N F B S N S N E
N M O X X V O M T V A G R O O T A T A G
Q Y N R U H A V I V T H D C R E N A W C
D R O C K E T R A C C O O N P U O R A T
L R E C U C A G O C S O N A H T R L X X
W E A D B T E P O M O O N V K O E O A O
J M N X G R U I X J A R M D V N J R L B
R O S M S L N K B Y P G P U A Q U D L Q
Y L W O M I L A N O S I W S X W Y B J O
T D Z N U T H J B P S F M A Z D S O W E
```

**ROCKET ACCOON** ☐

**STAR-LORD** ☐

**NOVA CORPS** ☐

**THANOS** ☐

**RONAN** ☐

**MILANO** ☐

**YONDU** ☐

**GROOT** ☐

**GAMORA** ☐

**DRAX** ☐

Answers on page 61

Answers on page 61

1 QUAD BLASTER

5 PROBE DROIDS

5 COSMIC CLAWS

3 BLASTER MOUNTS

# BIG EGO!

What if these super heroes were planets, just like Ego the Living Planet! Can you guess who each planet is?

**1.**

**2.**

**3.**

- ANT-MAN
- DRAX
- IRON MAN
- GROOT
- ROCKET RACCOON

**4.**

**5.**

**FACTOID!**

Ego the Living Planet is an ancient and highly intelligent life form. Rumour has it that he is Star-Lord's father!

ANSWERS ON PAGE 61

# SHIP SHAPE!

**ACTIVITY**

**A.**

**B.**

It's a race back to the ship! But who's gonna get the best seat? Only one route leads back to the Milano!

**C.**

**D.**

ANSWERS ON PAGE 61

25

ALL RIGHT, THAT'S 40 BALES OF XANDARIAN WHEAT, AT 40 PERCENT OFF THE MARKET PRICE.

PROBABLY BEST NOT TO ASK HOW WE MADE THAT HAPPEN.

BELIEVE ME, WE DIDN'T PLAN TO.

"GESUNDHEIT, HANG ON TIGHT!

PAUL ALLOR WRITER

ADAM ARCH ARTIST

CHARLIE KIRCHOFF COLORIST

VC's JC LETTERING

SEBASTIAN GIRNER & JON MOISA EDITORS MARK PANICCIA SENIOR EDITO AXEL ALONSO EDITOR IN CHIEF JOE QUESADA CHIEF CREATIVE OFFICER DAN BUCKLEY PUBLISHER ALAN FINE EXECUTIVE PRODUCER

SPECIAL THANKS TO HENRY ONG & PRODUCT FACTORY

I STILL DON'T UNDERSTAND, PETER. THIS IS A FARMING PLANET. WHY DO YOU HAVE GRAINS SMUGGLED IN?

SHIPPED IN, GAMORA!

IT IS NOT BY CHOICE. OUR VILLAGE IS FACING A TERRIBLE DROUGHT. THESE CANALS SHOULD BE FILLED WITH WATER, FROM THE OCEAN. BUT THE SEA LEVEL IS LOWER THAN IT HAS EVER BEEN.

THE CANALS ARE DRY, AND THE FIELDS SIT EMPTY.

PERHAPS IF YOU COULD SPARE A BIT MORE TIME, TO HELP US--

BOY, THAT SOUNDS LIKE SOMETHING WE'D LOVE TO DO, BUT WE SHOULD REALLY BE GETTING BACK TO THE SHIP. THERE'S A SICK CREW MEMBER ON BOARD.

I'M SORRY TO HEAR THAT! IS IT SERIOUS?

OH, NO. NOTHING TO WORRY ABOUT.

"IT'S JUST A LITTLE COLD."

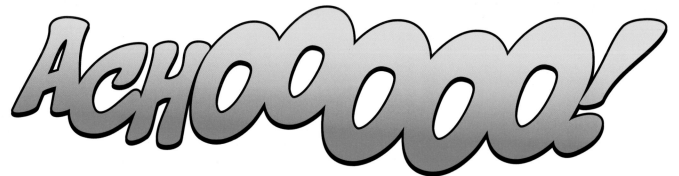

SO, DRAX...

YOU HAVE SOME SORT OF AN EXPLANATION FOR WHAT JUST HAPPENED?

I SUSPECT IT MAY HAVE SOMETHING TO DO WITH MY *LAST* VISIT TO THIS PLANET.

"I WAS HERE FOR A COMPETITION IN UNARMED COMBAT. EVERY FARMER AND VILLAGER FROM MILES AROUND CAME OUT TO WATCH.

"AFTERWARDS, WE CELEBRATED.

"THE CELEBRATION WENT ON FOR SEVERAL DAYS.

"IT MAY HAVE GONE ON FOR TOO LONG."

I WAS NOT INVOLVED IN THE DESTRUCTION, BUT I WAS BLAMED ANYWAY.

DRAX, WHY DIDN'T YOU TELL US ALL OF THIS *BEFORE* WE LANDED?

IT'S BEEN SEVERAL YEARS. I DID NOT THINK THEY WOULD STILL BE UPSET.

SERIOUSLY? YOU--DRAX THE DESTROYER--DIDN'T THINK THEY WOULD *HOLD A GRUDGE?*

I MEAN, NO OFFENSE, DUDE, BUT HOLDING GRUDGES IS KIND OF YOUR *THING.*

ACHOOOOO!

THAT AND *SNEEZING!* HOLDING GRUDGES AND SNEEZING. *THOSE* ARE YOUR THINGS!

I AM GROOT!

THAT'S RIGHT! GRAB AS MANY PIECES AS YOU CAN!

I AM GROOT!

YES, THEY'RE ALL IMPORTANT! THEY'RE ALL *PART* OF THE SHIP!

WE CAN'T TAKE ANY MORE OF THIS! WE ONLY HAVE SO MUCH SHIP TO LOSE!

DON'T WORRY, ROCKET. WE'RE COMING UP ON ANOTHER VILLAGE! WITH ANY LUCK, THEY'LL BE MORE...

...FRIENDLY.

THE VILLAGERS MUST HAVE SPREAD THE WORD THAT THE DESTROYER IS HERE. THERE TRULY IS NOWHERE TO LAND.

THEN WE JUST NEED TO FIND A PLACE WHERE NO ONE LIVES. AND IF THIS PLANET IS ANYTHING LIKE THE ONE I'M FROM, THAT MEANS...

"WAY NORTH.

ACHOOOOO!

"DRAX'S SKIN IS THICK ENOUGH THAT THE WEATHER WON'T BOTHER HIM. WE CAN JUST LEAVE HIM THERE, UNTIL THE SNEEZING PASSES.

"AND WHO KNOWS..."

SPLASH

FATHER!

"IT MIGHT EVEN *HELP* WITH THIS PLANET'S LITTLE WATER PROBLEM."

LATER.

I'M NOT SAYIN' WE MANAGED TO FIND EVERY LITTLE PIECE THAT FELL OFF. BUT WE GOT MOST OF THEM, AND PATCHED UP THE REST. SHIP'S AS GOOD AS NEW.

ASSUMING IT WAS IN TERRIBLE, *TERRIBLE* SHAPE WHEN IT WAS NEW.

ALRIGHT. I GUESS NOW WE JUST HAVE TO HOPE DRAX NEVER GETS SICK AGAIN. LIKE...*EVER.*

WHICH IS UNLIKELY, GIVEN HIS EATING HABITS.

WHOA! LET'S NOT GO TALKIN' ABOUT CHANGING DRAX'S EATING HABITS, OKAY? WE DON'T WANNA PUT IDEAS IN HIS HEAD.

WELL, *SOMETHING* MADE HIM SICK. AND UNLESS YOU WANT TO REPAIR THE SHIP'S HULL ALL OVER AGAIN--

HEY, I'M JUST SAYIN' THAT AS LONG AS DRAX AIN'T EATIN' *ME,* HIS EATIN' HABITS ARE JUST *FINE!*

THE END!

Power down the boosters. There's a transmission coming through but it's in an alien language. You'll have to use the translation modulator:

## INCOMING TRANSMISSION

ANSWERS ON PAGE 61

### TRANSLATION MODULATOR

C E G H I L M N O R S T U V W Y

### TRANSLATED MESSAGE

Huh? That last message can't be right? Anyhow, let's see what these aliens have to offer. We need supplies!

What are we missing from the first inventory compared to the second? Colour in the extra items.

TRADING INTERFACE

Right let's get outta here. **HEY! WHAT"S HAPPENING TO ROCKET AND GROOT? THEY'RE BEING TELEPORTED!!!**

Where will Rocket and Groot end up? Turn to page 46 to find out!

# BATTLE READY!

Star-Lord's got back-up and the rest of the Guardians are ready for action! Can you spot all seven differences between these two scenes?

GROO

# WEAPON UP!

**Help Rocket Raccoon find three matching pairs of weapons from his arsenal.**

*Circle the three matching pairs*

ANSWERS ON PAGE 61

# GROO

The last surviving member of a tree-like alien race, Groot is perhaps one of the most unusual beings in all the cosmos. Though calm and quiet in most instances, he is known to unleash his tremendous strength on any enemy foolish enough to threaten his allies, particularly his longtime partner in crime, Rocket.

## HOMEWORLD

### BANISHED!
Groot originates from Planet X - where he was outcast by his fellow tree beings for standing up for the weak.

## SAY WHAT?!

I AM... ...GROOT.

Though he can just say the phrase, "I am Groot," only Rocket, as far as we've seen, can understand Groot's exact meaning.

Groot is almost indestructible! He can regrow himself entirely from just a small shoot.

i am groot!

**NAME:** GROOT
**SPECIES:** FLORA COLOSSI
**SKILLS:** NEAR GENIUS LEVEL
INTELLIGENCE
SUPERHUMAN STRENGTH
PLANT-LIKE FORM ENABLES
HIM TO RESHAPE HIS LIMBS
OR REGROW DAMAGE.
CAN EMIT GLOWING SPORES
**LIKES:** ROCKET RACCOON
**DISLIKES:** BULLIES

# GETTIN' MAD!

And you thought the Hulk was scary when he's angry. Groot takes it to a whole new level and can grow limbs to attack with!

# BEST OF FRIENDS

Two spacefaring loners became the inseparable buddies when Groot and Rocket Raccoon met. In truth, they were both captured by space pirates and teamed-up to escape!

# ROCKET'S WORKSHOP

He's the gun totin' explosive weapon-smith that is **ROCKET RACCOON** and there's a whole lotta tinkerin' goin' on in his workshop. Wanna help him? **Let's go!**

## GET A GRIP!

**1.** Star-Lord wants his blaster back, but Rocket can't remember which one was his original. **Can you match it up and find the right one?**

ORIGINAL

A.

B.

C.

# MISS ME?

Aww heck this **IONIC ACCELERATOR** has some kickin' power!
But which shot is on target to hit the alien freighter?

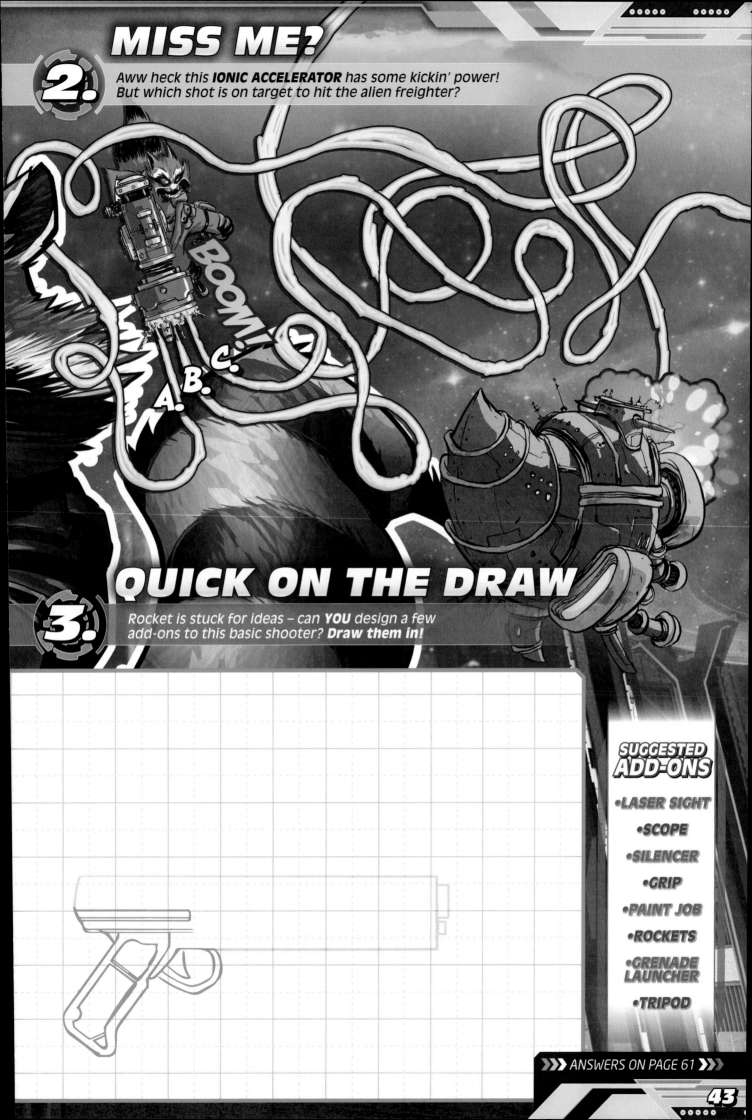

**BOOM!**

A. B. C.

# QUICK ON THE DRAW

**3.**

Rocket is stuck for ideas – can **YOU** design a few
add-ons to this basic shooter? **Draw them in!**

## SUGGESTED ADD-ONS

- LASER SIGHT
- SCOPE
- SILENCER
- GRIP
- PAINT JOB
- ROCKETS
- GRENADE LAUNCHER
- TRIPOD

ANSWERS ON PAGE 61

# BLOCKADE!

Star-Lord's going to need all his skill to get past this Kree blockade! Can you guide him through the asteroid belt without coming into contact with any of the spacecraft?

START

FINISH

ANSWERS ON PAGE 61

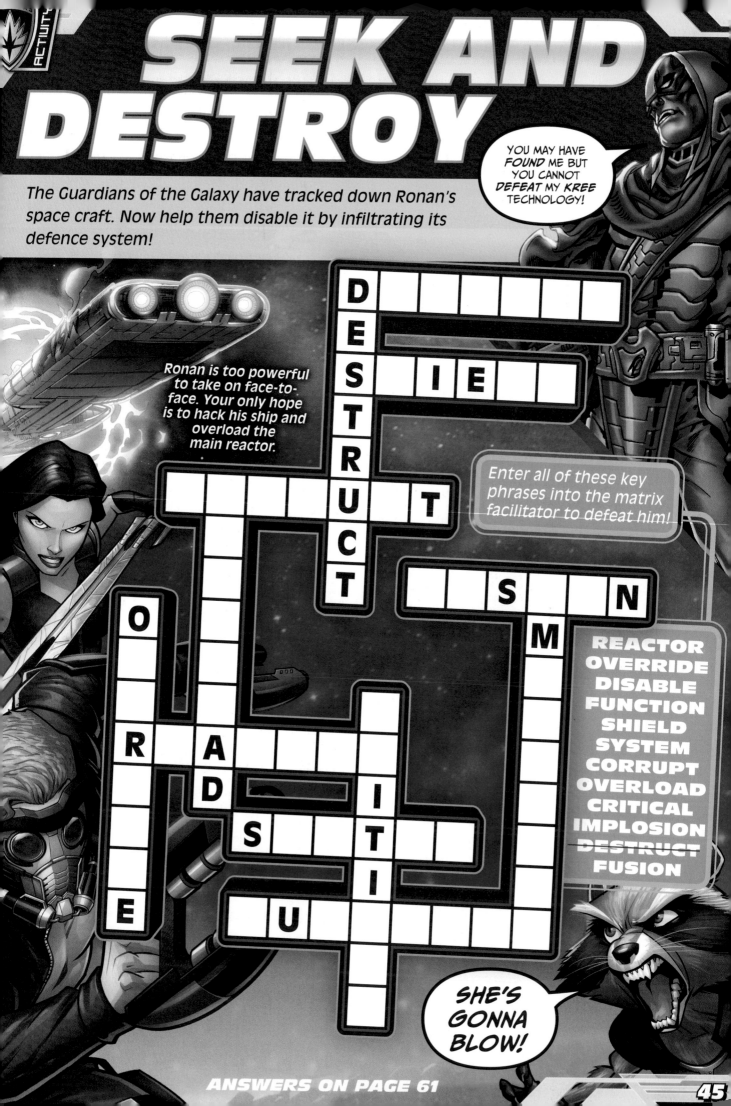

# SEEK AND DESTROY

The Guardians of the Galaxy have tracked down Ronan's space craft. Now help them disable it by infiltrating its defence system!

YOU MAY HAVE *FOUND* ME BUT YOU CANNOT *DEFEAT MY KREE* TECHNOLOGY!

Ronan is too powerful to take on face-to-face. Your only hope is to hack his ship and overload the main reactor.

Enter all of these key phrases into the matrix facilitator to defeat him!

REACTOR
OVERRIDE
DISABLE
FUNCTION
SHIELD
SYSTEM
CORRUPT
OVERLOAD
CRITICAL
IMPLOSION
DESTRUCT
FUSION

SHE'S GONNA BLOW!

ANSWERS ON PAGE 61

45

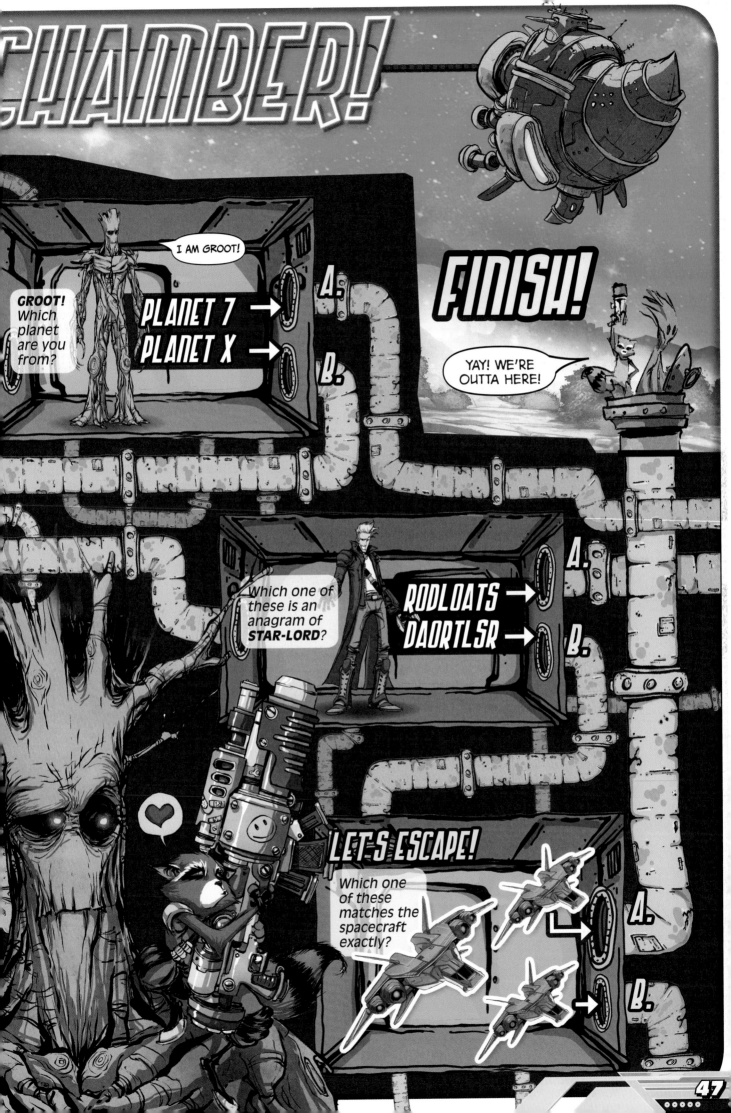

"DRAX THE DESTROYER!"

BASED ON THE ANIMATED SHORT

ADAPTED BY JOE CARAMAGNA

"...I WILL NOT *HARM* HIM."

AS WE ENTER THE FINAL ROUND OF COMBAT, THE DESTROYER FACES HIS TOUGHEST CHALLENGER YET!

CLANK!

WHOOSH!

WHOOSH!

NO SURPRISE SINCE THERE'S A LOT AT STAKE!

THE CHAMPION WILL EARN THE RIGHT TO SERVE AS ENFORCER AND STAND AT THE RIGHT HAND OF *RONAN THE ACCUSER!*

CLANK!

CLINK!

HNN!

WHUDD!

IT'S ALL OVER BUT THE SLAYING--

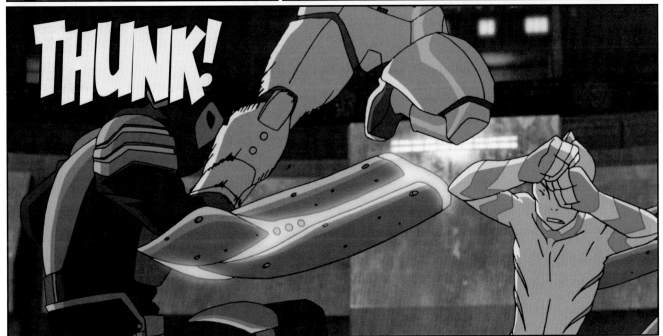

THE END

# FLIGHT

## IN A FIX!

The thrust capacitor needs replacing!
Can you see which one will fit the space?

ORIGINAL THRUST CAPACITOR

A. ☐

B. ☐

C. ☐

## YOU'RE FIRED!

Rocket's lost his prototype weapon! Can you draw him a new one?

# DECK

## ENTWINED!

Groot's been spreading his branches all round my ship! Can you help me find which one leads to him? Betcha can't find it first time!

**A.** ☐

**B.** ☐

**C.** ☐

The monitor's playing up - Drax has no colour!

Can you fix this with some colouring enhancements?

**ANSWERS ON PAGE 61**

# DRAW DRAX

Help to tame **DRAX THE DESTROYER** by tracing over the lines and colouring him in. Be careful... he's easily angered...

COLOUR REFERENCE

NAME
DRAX

# ANSWERS

## 18
SIGNAL TRACER

RONAN

## 21 SEARCH THE STARS!

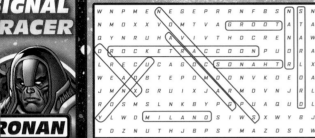

Words found: GROOT, ROCKET RACCOON, MILANO

## 22 YONDU'S RAVAGER HUNT!

## 24 BIG EGO

1. IRON MAN
2. DRAX
3. GROOT
4. ANT-MAN
5. ROCKET RACCOON

## 25 SHIP SHAPE

C

## 36

D

### INCOMING TRANSMISSION

**TRANSLATED MESSAGE**

WELCOME YOU WILL GIVE US THE TREE AND RACCOON

**TRADING INTERFACE**

## ACTION STATIONS

## 38 BATTLE READY!

## 39 WEAPON UP!

## 42 ROCKET'S WORKSHOP!

1. B

2. C

## 44 BLOCKADE!

## 45 SEEK AND DESTROY

DISABLE
SHIELD
DESTRUCT
CORRUPT
OVERLOAD
FUSION
OVERRIDE
REACTOR
CRITICAL
IMPLOSION
SYSTEM
FUNCTION

## 46 ENTER THE CRYOMORPH CHAMBER!

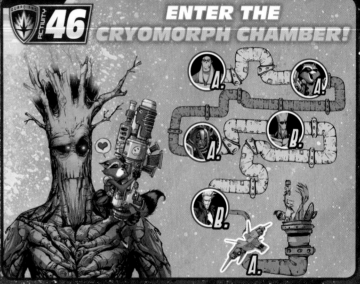

A.
A.
A.
B.
B.
A.

## 58 FLIGHT DECK

ENTWINED!

B.

IN A FIX!

B.